Gamesroom
ages 9 +

Bedroom
ages 6 – 9

Playroom
ages 4 – 7

Nursery
ages 1 – 4

Our Bloomsbury House has a
special room for each age group –
this one is from the Nursery

Ask to see more titles
from your room

All rights reserved. No part of this publication may be reproduced or transmitted by any means, electronic, mechanical, photocopying or otherwise without the prior permission of the publisher.
First published in France in 1996 by Albin Michel Jeunesse, 22, rue Huyghens, 75014 Paris
First published in Great Britain in 1996
Bloomsbury Publishing Plc, 2 Soho Square, London W1V 6HB
Copyright © Text and Illustrations Isabelle Carrier 1996
The moral rights of the author and illustrator have been asserted
A CIP catalogue record for this book
is available from the British Library
ISBN 0 7475 2711 3
Printed in Italy
10 9 8 7 6 5 4 3 2 1

The world is full of COLOURS

ISABELLE CARRIER

Bloomsbury Children's Books

a snake

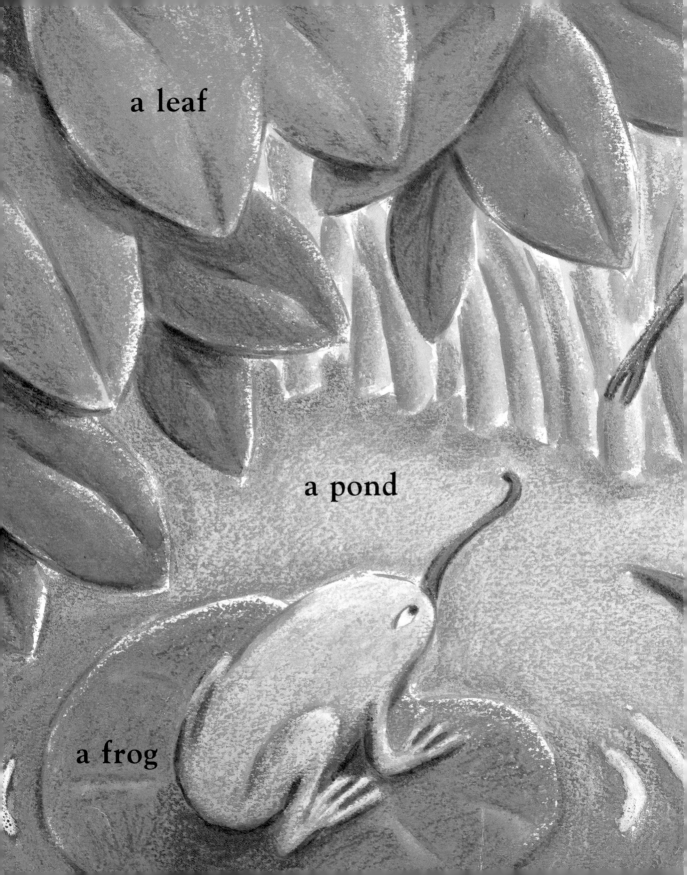

GREEN

as...

BROWN
as...

a squirrel

a tree trunk

a bear

a hazelnut

the grassland in summer

the ploughed earth

a ladybird

a strawberry

a carp

RED
as...

a field of poppies

the sea

a parrot

a blue whale

BLUE

as...

the sky

a snow drop

a white rabbit

a swan

WHITE
as...

the snow in winter

a flamingo

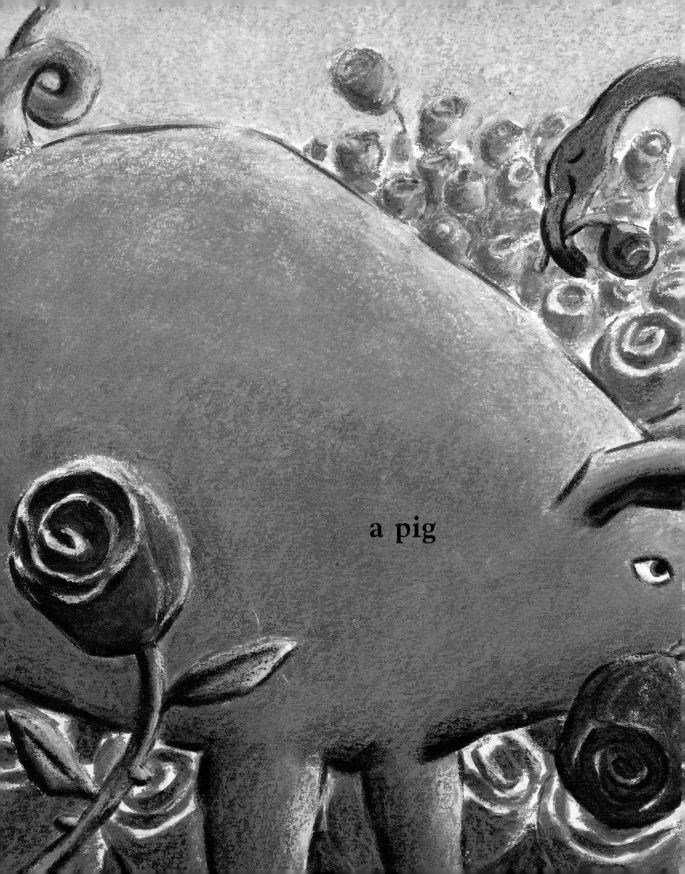

a pig

PINK
as...

a garden of roses

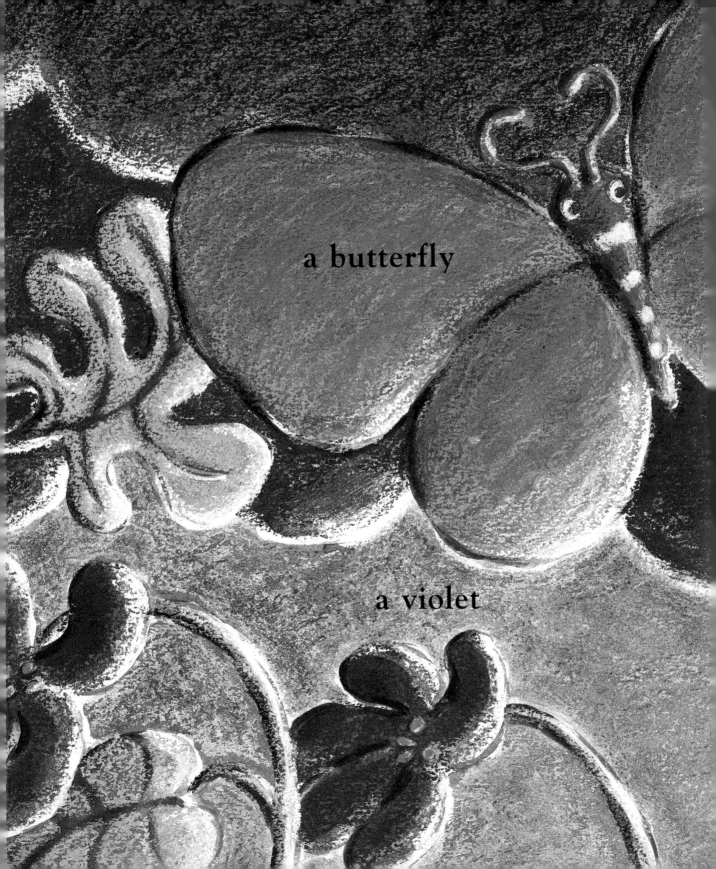

a butterfly

a violet

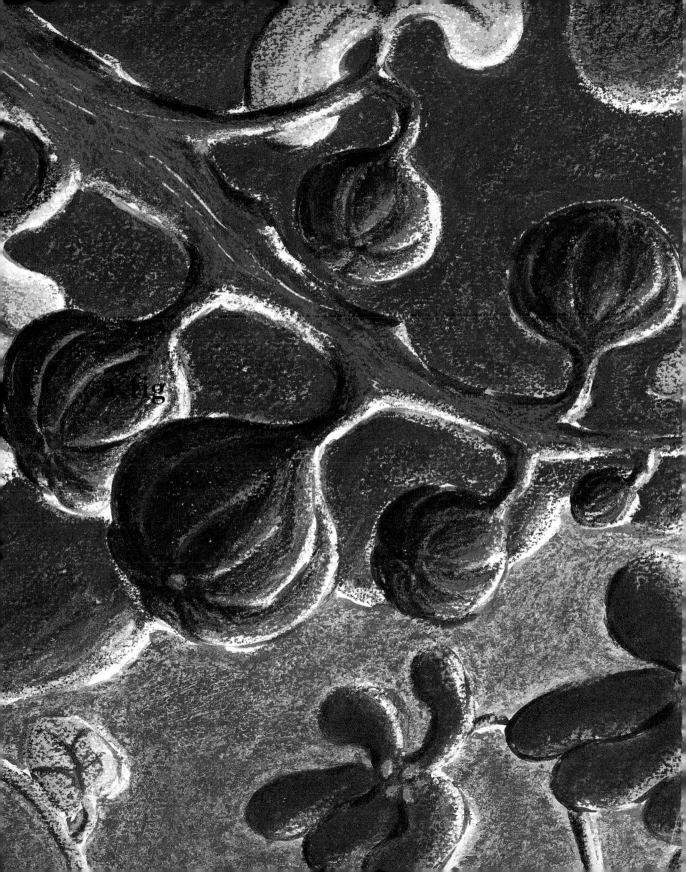

a fig

PURPLE

as...

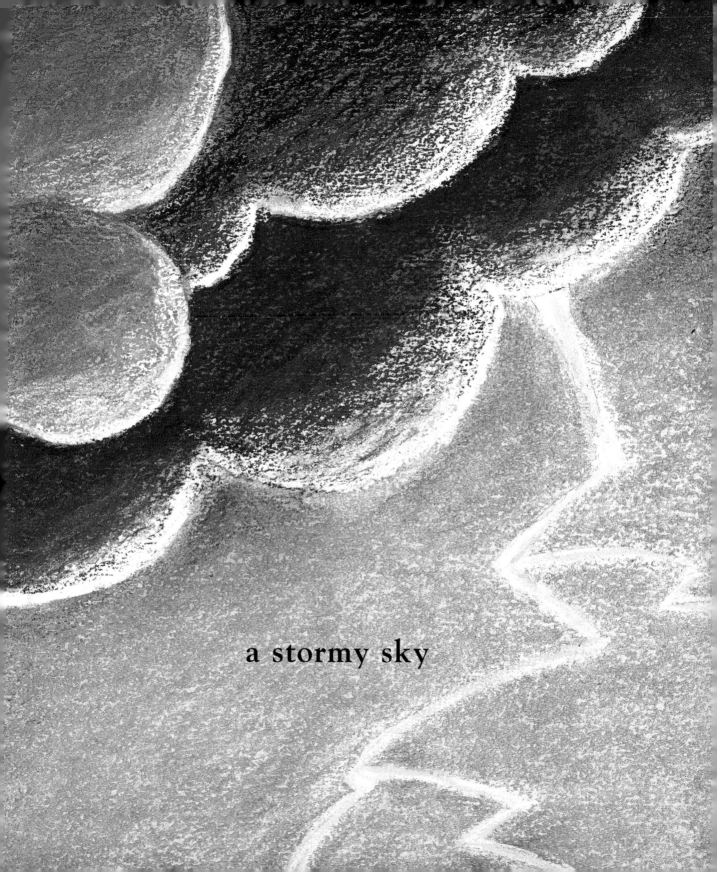

a stormy sky

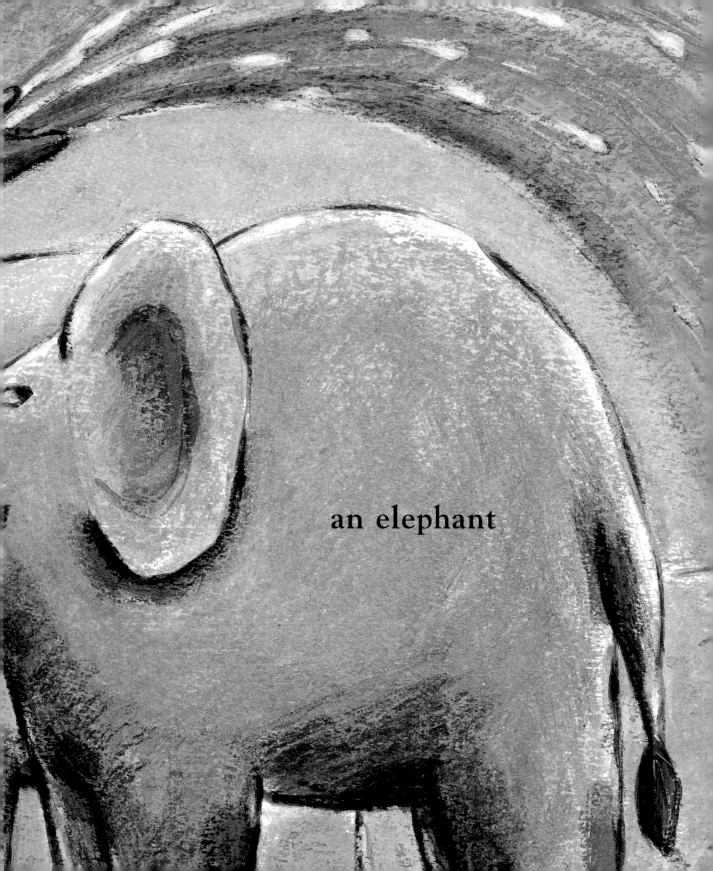

an elephant

GREY
as...

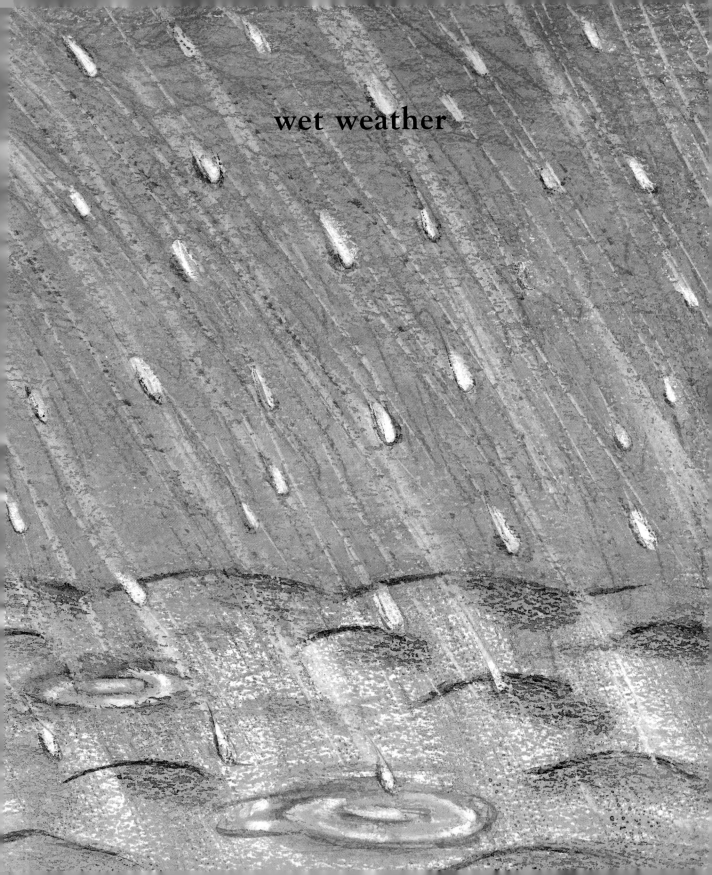

wet weather

a fox

autumn leaves

a slug

ORANGE
as…

the sunset

a camel

the sun

a sunflower

YELLOW

as...

the great sandy wilderness

a crow

an ant

a panther

BLACK

as...

BEAUTIFUL

as....

the night

all the colours in the world.